French Horn
Scales, Arpeggios & Exercises

for Trinity College London exams from 2015

Grades 1-8

Published by:
Trinity College London
www.trinitycollege.com

Registered in the UK
Company no. 02683033
Charity no. 1014792

Copyright © 2014 Trinity College London
First impression, August 2014

Photo: Zute Lightfoot, French horn courtesy of Yamaha Music London

Printed in Great Britain by Caligraving Ltd.

Contents

Introduction

This book contains all the scales, arpeggios and exercises listed in Trinity's Brass syllabus for French horn.

At each grade you will find the lip flexibility exercises (section i), scales & arpeggios (section ii) and the exercises (section iii, Grades 1-5 only) which may be presented as an alternative to scales. In the exam, exercises can be played from the music while lip flexibility exercises and scales must be performed from memory.

Lip flexibility exercises, besides being extremely useful for sound and stamina development, also make excellent warm-ups and the use of different exercises chosen from across the grades will help all students in their daily practice. Advanced students are encouraged to extend the range of the early exercises when using them as warm-ups.

The scales are presented grouped by key and arranged from C-B. The syllabus has been devised in a way which will develop a deepening understanding of tonal centres. The range and complexity of material to be learnt within a given tonal centre increases with each grade.

The exercises (in section iii, which may be presented in place of scales), are based on the same tonal centres as the scales. Candidates preparing the scales are advised also to practise the exercises to help familiarise themselves with the tonal centres. Candidates presenting the exercises will also benefit from practising the scales.

The tempo ranges shown in the book are taken from the syllabus and are intended to cover all brass instruments; technical work should be prepared at a consistent speed appropriate to the instrument. For most instruments, scales and arpeggios should be prepared in a single breath; where an extra breath is necessary this should be taken in a musically logical place, usually at the top of the exercise. For the purposes of fulfilling exam criteria, fluency, accuracy and evenness of tone should be regarded as equally important aspects of technical competence.

Candidates are advised always to check the current syllabus for exact requirements of the exam.

Grade 1

Candidates to prepare i) Lip flexibility exercise				
Lip flexibility exercise (from memory) Play the exercise slurred, using the valve combinations given.				
Candidates to prepare in full *either* section ii) *or* section iii)				
either **ii) Scales & arpeggios** (from memory) − the examiner will select from the following:				
Scales: C major A minor (candidate's choice of natural *or* harmonic *or* melodic minor)	one octave	♩=46–60	tongued	*mf*
Arpeggios: C major A minor				
or **iii) Exercises** (music may be used)				
Candidates to prepare 1a *or* 1b; 2a *or* 2b; and 3a *or* 3b (three exercises in total). The candidate will choose one exercise to play first; the examiner will then select one of the remaining two prepared exercises to be performed.				
1a. Let's Play! *or* 1b. Threesy-peasy		for finger technique		
2a. March to the Top *or* 2b. The Football Chant		for articulation		
3a. I am an Elephant *or* 3b. Creeping		for breath control *or* rhythm		

i) Lip flexibility exercise

F Horn − descending

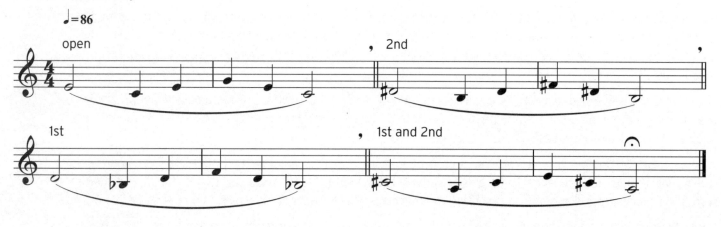

or

B♭ Horn − descending

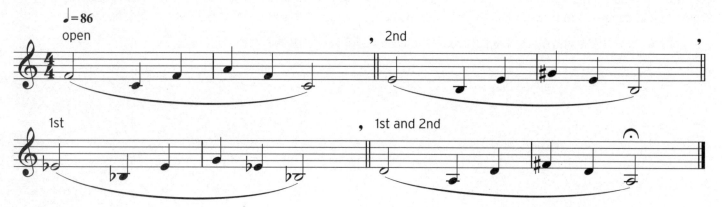

ii) Scales & arpeggios

C major scale (one octave)

C major arpeggio (one octave)

A natural minor scale (one octave)

A harmonic minor scale (one octave)

A melodic minor scale (one octave)

A minor arpeggio (one octave)

iii) Exercises

1a. Let's Play! – finger technique

1b. Threesy-peasy – finger technique

2a. March to the Top – articulation

2b. The Football Chant – articulation

3a. I am an Elephant – breath control

3b. Creeping – rhythm

Grade 2

Candidates to prepare i) Lip flexibility exercise				
Lip flexibility exercise (from memory) Play the exercise slurred, using the valve combinations given.				
Candidates to prepare in full *either* section ii) *or* section iii)				
either **ii) Scales & arpeggios** (from memory) – the examiner will select from the following:				
Scales: D and B♭ major B minor (candidate's choice of natural *or* harmonic *or* melodic minor)	one octave	♩=50-66	tongued *or* slurred as requested by the examiner	*mf*
Arpeggios: D and B♭ major B minor				
or **iii) Exercises** (music may be used)				
Candidates to prepare 1a *or* 1b; 2a *or* 2b; and 3a *or* 3b (three exercises in total). The candidate will choose one exercise to play first; the examiner will then select one of the remaining two prepared exercises to be performed.				
1a. Hand-bell Peal *or* 1b. Calypso and So		for finger technique		
2a. Lolloping *or* 2b. Sneakers		for articulation		
3a. Eastern Promise *or* 3b. Jumper		for breath control *or* rhythm		

i) Lip flexibility exercise

F Horn – descending

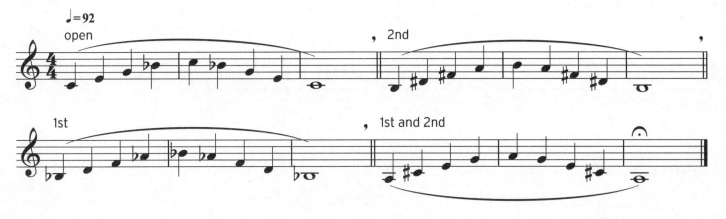

or

B♭ Horn – descending

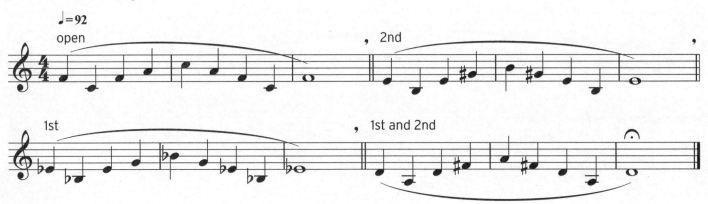

ii) Scales & arpeggios

D major scale (one octave)

D major arpeggio (one octave)

B♭ major scale (one octave)

B♭ major arpeggio (one octave)

B harmonic minor scale (one octave)

B natural minor scale (one octave)

B melodic minor scale (one octave)

B minor arpeggio (one octave)

iii) Exercises

1a. Hand-bell Peal – finger technique

1b. Calypso and So – finger technique

2a. Lolloping – articulation

2b. Sneakers – articulation

Moderato ♩ = 76

3a. Eastern Promise – breath control

Mysterioso ♩ = 63

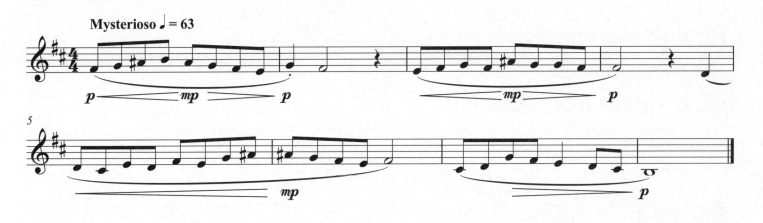

3b. Jumper – rhythm

Allegretto ♩ = 108 *(may be played with a swing feel)*

Grade 3

Candidates to prepare i) Lip flexibility exercise				
Lip flexibility exercise (from memory) Play the exercise slurred, using the valve combinations given.				
Candidates to prepare in full *either* section ii) *or* section iii)				
either **ii) Scales & arpeggios** (from memory) − the examiner will select from the following:				
Scales: Eb and G (lower octave) major C and D minor (candidate's choice of *either* harmonic *or* melodic minor)	one octave	♩ = 54-72	tongued *or* slurred as requested by the examiner	*mf*
Whole-tone scale starting on C				
Arpeggios: Eb and G major C and D minor				
or **iii) Exercises** (music may be used)				
Candidates to prepare 1a *or* 1b; 2a *or* 2b; and 3a *or* 3b (three exercises in total). The candidate will choose one exercise to play first; the examiner will then select one of the remaining two prepared exercises to be performed.				
1a. Let's Rock! *or* 1b. Ambling Along	for finger technique			
2a. Stately Dance *or* 2b. Mouse Meets Elephant	for articulation			
3a. Balloon Ride *or* 3b. The Sleepwalking Robot	for breath control			

i) Lip flexibility exercise

F Horn − descending

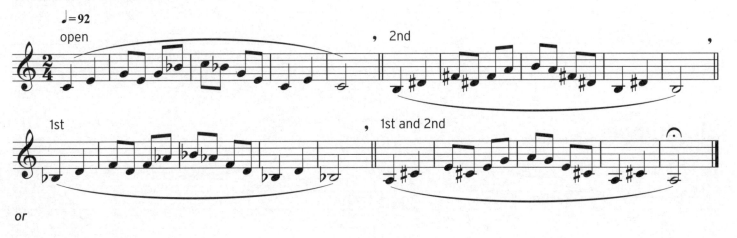

or

Bb Horn − descending

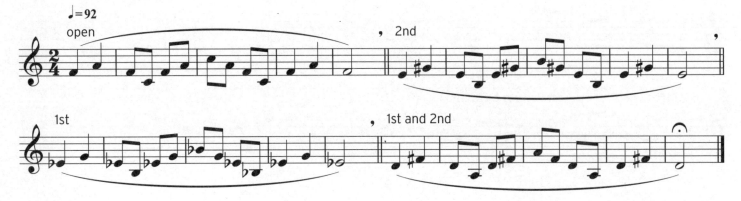

ii) Scales & arpeggios

C harmonic minor scale (one octave)

C melodic minor scale (one octave)

C minor arpeggio (one octave)

Whole-tone scale starting on C (one octave)

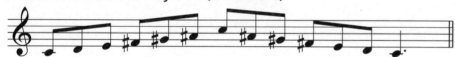

D harmonic minor scale (one octave)

D melodic minor scale (one octave)

D minor arpeggio (one octave)

13

Grade 3 continued

Eb major scale (one octave)

Eb major arpeggio (one octave)

G major scale (one octave)

G major arpeggio (one octave)

iii) Exercises

1a. Let's Rock! – finger technique

1b. Ambling Along – finger technique

Moderato ♩ = 84 *(may be played with a swing feel)*

2a. Stately Dance – articulation

Andante ♩ = 84

2b. Mouse Meets Elephant – articulation

Moderato ♩ = 84

3a. Balloon Ride – breath control

3b. The Sleepwalking Robot – breath control

Grade 4

Candidates to prepare i) Lip flexibility exercise				
Lip flexibility exercise (from memory) Play the exercise slurred, using the valve combinations given.				

Candidates to prepare in full *either* section ii) *or* section iii)

either **ii) Scales & arpeggios** (from memory) – the examiner will select from the following:

Scales: F major F minor (candidate's choice of *either* harmonic *or* melodic minor)	two octaves	♩ = 60-104	tongued *or* slurred as requested by the examiner	*mf*
Whole-tone scale starting on F				
E major E minor (candidate's choice of *either* harmonic *or* melodic minor)	one octave			
Chromatic scale starting on C				
Arpeggios: F major F minor	two octaves			
E major E minor	one octave			

or **iii) Exercises** (music may be used)

Candidates to prepare 1a *or* 1b; 2a *or* 2b; and 3a *or* 3b (three exercises in total).
The candidate will choose one exercise to play first; the examiner will then select one of the remaining two prepared exercises to be performed.

1a. Rescue Squad	*or*	1b. Bob-tail Bob	for finger technique
2a. Let in Latin	*or*	2b. After the Battle	for articulation
3a. Jigsaw Peace	*or*	3b. Sliding Down the Banister	for breath control

i) Lip flexibility exercise

Grade 4 continued

ii) Scales & arpeggios

Chromatic scale starting on C (one octave)

E major scale (one octave)

E major arpeggio (one octave)

E harmonic minor scale (one octave)

E melodic minor scale (one octave)

E minor arpeggio (one octave)

F major scale (two octaves)

F major arpeggio (two octaves)

F harmonic minor scale (two octaves)

F melodic minor scale (two octaves)

F minor arpeggio (two octaves)

Whole-tone scale starting on F (two octaves)

iii) Exercises

1a. Rescue Squad – finger technique

Moderato (with urgency) ♩ = 120

1b. Bob-tail Bob – finger technique

2a. Let in Latin – articulation

2b. After the Battle – articulation

3a. Jigsaw Peace – breath control

3b. Sliding Down the Banister – breath control

Grade 5

Candidates to prepare i) Lip flexibility exercise

Lip flexibility exercise (from memory)
Play the exercise slurred, using the valve combinations given.

Candidates to prepare in full *either* section ii) *or* section iii)

either **ii) Scales & arpeggios** (from memory) − the examiner will select from the following:

Scales: G major G and E♭ minor (candidate's choice of *either* harmonic *or* melodic minor)	two octaves			
Whole-tone scale starting on G Chromatic scale starting on G		♩ = 66-112	tongued *or* slurred as requested by the examiner	*mf*
A♭ major C♯ minor (candidate's choice of *either* harmonic *or* melodic minor)	one octave			
Arpeggios: G major G and E♭ minor	two octaves			
A♭ major C♯ minor Dominant 7th in the key of G	one octave			

or **iii) Exercises** (music may be used)

Candidates to prepare 1a *or* 1b; 2a *or* 2b; and 3a *or* 3b (three exercises in total).
The candidate will choose one exercise to play first; the examiner will then select one of the remaining two prepared exercises to be performed.

1a. Jump Start	*or*	1b. Ta Aunt Ella!	for octave leaps *or* finger technique
2a. Tongue-go	*or*	2b. Sonority Rules	for articulation *or* low playing
3a. Smooth Strides	*or*	3b. Finding the Pulse	for breath control *or* rhythm

i) Lip flexibility exercise

F Horn − descending

♩ = 120

open

Repeat using the following valve combinations:

2nd − 1st − 1st and 2nd

or

B♭ Horn − descending

♩ = 120

open

Repeat using the following valve combinations:

2nd − 1st − 1st and 2nd

ii) Scales & arpeggios

C# harmonic minor scale (one octave)

C# melodic minor scale (one octave)

C# minor arpeggio (one octave)

Eb harmonic minor scale (two octaves)

Eb melodic minor scale (two octaves)

Eb minor arpeggio (two octaves)

G major scale (two octaves)

Grade 5 continued

G major arpeggio (two octaves)

G harmonic minor scale (two octaves)

G melodic minor scale (two octaves)

G minor arpeggio (two octaves)

Chromatic scale starting on G (two octaves)

Whole-tone scale starting on G (two octaves)

Dominant 7th in the key of G (one octave)

A♭ major scale (one octave)

A♭ major arpeggio (one octave)

iii) Exercises

1a. Jump Start – octave leaps

1b. Ta Aunt Ella! – finger technique

Grade 5 continued

2a. Tongue-go – articulation

2b. Sonority Rules – low playing

3a. Smooth Strides – breath control

3b. Finding the Pulse – rhythm

Grade 6

Candidates to prepare i) Lip flexibility exercise and chromatic scale				
Lip flexibility exercise (from memory) Play the exercise slurred, using the valve combinations given. Chromatic scale starting on A♭ (two octaves, from memory) (tempo, dynamics and articulation as for scales below)				

Candidates to prepare in full *either* section ii) *or* section iii)				
either **ii) Scales & arpeggios** (from memory) – the examiner will select from the following:				
Candidates should prepare scales and arpeggios from the following tonal centres: A♭ major, G♯ minor D major, D minor	two octaves	♩ = 72–120	tongued, slurred *or* staccato-tongued as requested by the examiner	*f* or *p*
Plus: Whole-tone scale starting on D Dominant 7th in the key of G Diminished 7th starting on D Augmented arpeggio starting on D				

When the examiner requests a **major tonal centre**, the candidate should play in succession:
    The major scale
    The major arpeggio
 	
When the examiner requests a **minor tonal centre**, the candidate should play in succession:
    The melodic minor scale
    The harmonic minor scale
    The minor arpeggio				

or **iii) Orchestral extracts** See current syllabus for details				

i) Lip flexibility exercise and chromatic scale

F Horn – descending

Repeat using the following valve combinations:

2nd – 1st – 1st and 2nd

or

B♭ Horn – descending

Repeat using the following valve combinations:

2nd – 1st – 1st and 2nd

Chromatic scale starting on A♭ (two octaves)

ii) Scales & arpeggios

D major scale (two octaves)

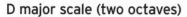

D major arpeggio (two octaves)

D harmonic minor scale (two octaves)

D melodic minor scale (two octaves)

D minor arpeggio (two octaves)

Whole-tone scale starting on D (two octaves)

Grade 6 continued

Augmented arpeggio starting on D (two octaves)

Diminished 7th starting on D (two octaves)

Dominant 7th in the key of G (two octaves)

A♭ major scale (two octaves)

A♭ major arpeggio (two octaves)

G# harmonic minor scale (two octaves)

G# melodic minor scale (two octaves)

G# minor arpeggio (two octaves)

Grade 7

Candidates to prepare i) Lip flexibility exercise and chromatic scale

Lip flexibility exercise (from memory)
Play the exercise slurred, using the valve combinations given.
Chromatic scale starting on A (two octaves, from memory) (tempo, dynamics and articulation as for scales below)

Candidates to prepare in full *either* section ii) *or* section iii)

either **ii) Scales & arpeggios** (from memory) – the examiner will select from the following:

Candidates should prepare scales and arpeggios from the following tonal centres: B major, B minor A major, A minor	two octaves	♩ = 80-126	tongued, slurred *or* staccato-tongued as requested by the examiner	*f* or *mf* or *p* or crescendo/diminuendo (*p-f-p*) or diminuendo/crescendo (*f-p-f*)
Plus: Chromatic scale starting on B Whole-tone scale starting on A and B Dominant 7th in the keys of D and E Diminished 7th starting on A and B Augmented arpeggio starting on A and B				

When the examiner requests a **major tonal centre**, the candidate should play in succession:
    The major scale
    The major arpeggio

When the examiner requests a **minor tonal centre**, the candidate should play in succession:
    The melodic minor scale
    The harmonic minor scale
    The minor arpeggio

or **iii) Orchestral extracts**
See current syllabus for details

i) Lip flexibility exercise and chromatic scale

F Horn – descending

Repeat using the following valve combinations:

1st − 1st and 2nd − 2nd and 3rd (no 2nd valve)

or

B♭ Horn – descending

Repeat using the following valve combinations:

1st − 1st and 2nd − 2nd and 3rd (no 2nd valve)

Grade 7 continued

Chromatic scale starting on A (two octaves)

ii) Scales & arpeggios

Dominant 7th in the key of D (two octaves)

Dominant 7th in the key of E (two octaves)

A major scale (two octaves)

A major arpeggio (two octaves)

A harmonic minor scale (two octaves)

A melodic minor scale (two octaves)

A minor arpeggio (two octaves)

Whole-tone scale starting on A (two octaves)

Augmented arpeggio starting on A (two octaves)

Diminished 7th starting on A (two octaves)

B major scale – upper octave (two octaves)

B major arpeggio – upper octave (two octaves)

B harmonic minor scale – upper octave (two octaves)

Grade 7 continued

B melodic minor scale – upper octave (two octaves)

B minor arpeggio – upper octave (two octaves)

Chromatic scale starting on B – upper octave (two octaves)

Whole-tone scale starting on B – upper octave (two octaves)

Augmented arpeggio starting on B – upper octave (two octaves)

Diminished 7th starting on B – upper octave (two octaves)

Grade 8

Candidates to prepare i) Lip flexibility exercise and chromatic scale				
Lip flexibility exercise (from memory) Play the exercise slurred, using the valve combinations given. Chromatic scale starting on F# (two octaves, from memory) (tempo, dynamics and articulation as for scales below)				
Candidates to prepare in full *either* section ii) *or* section iii)				
either **ii) Scales & arpeggios** (from memory) – the examiner will select from the following:				
Candidates should prepare scales and arpeggios from the following tonal centres: Bb major, Bb minor	three octaves			
Candidates should prepare scales and arpeggios from the following tonal centres: Db major, C# minor F# major, F# minor	two octaves			*f* or *mf* or *p* or crescendo/ diminuendo (*p-f-p*) or diminuendo/ crescendo (*f-p-f*)
Plus: Whole-tone scale starting on Bb Dominant 7th in the key of Eb Diminished 7th starting on Bb	three octaves	♩=88-132	tongued, slurred *or* staccato-tongued as requested by the examiner	
Crabwise scale from Bb and F Dominant 7th in the key of B Diminished 7th starting on F# Augmented arpeggio starting on F# and Db	two octaves			
C major scale, hand stopped	one octave			

When the examiner requests a **major tonal centre**, the candidate should play in succession:
    The major scale
    The major arpeggio
 	
When the examiner requests a **minor tonal centre**, the candidate should play in succession:
    The melodic minor scale
    The harmonic minor scale
    The minor arpeggio				

or **iii) Orchestral extracts** See current syllabus for details				

i) Lip flexibility exercise and chromatic scale

F Horn – descending

♩.=112

open

Repeat using the following valve combinations:

1st – 1st and 2nd – 2nd and 3rd (no 2nd valve)

Grade 8 continued

or

Bb Horn – descending

♩=100

open

Repeat using the following valve combinations:

1st – 1st and 2nd – 2nd and 3rd (no 2nd valve)

Chromatic scale starting on F# (two octaves)

ii) Scales & arpeggios

Db major scale (two octaves)

Db major arpeggio (two octaves)

C# harmonic minor scale (two octaves)

C# melodic minor scale (two octaves)

C# minor arpeggio (two octaves)

Augmented arpeggio starting on D♭ (two octaves)

Dominant 7th in the key of E♭ (three octaves)

F# major scale (two octaves)

F# major arpeggio (two octaves)

F# harmonic minor scale (two octaves)

Grade 8 continued

F# melodic minor scale (two octaves)

F# minor arpeggio (two octaves)

Augmented arpeggio starting on F# (two octaves)

Diminished 7th starting on F# (two octaves)

B♭ major scale (three octaves)

B♭ major arpeggio (three octaves)

Bb harmonic minor scale (three octaves)

Bb melodic minor scale (three octaves)

Bb minor arpeggio (three octaves)

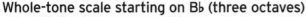

Whole-tone scale starting on Bb (three octaves)

Diminished 7th starting on Bb (three octaves)

Dominant 7th in the key of B (two octaves)

Grade 8 continued

Crabwise scale from F (two octaves – tongued or slurred as indicated)

Crabwise scale from B♭ (two octaves – tongued or slurred as indicated)

(the candidate may choose to play this exercise at the lower octave)

C major scale (one octave) – to be played hand-stopped

(scale to be stopped only; hand horn technique is not required)